# WE THREE KINGS...

Brian Moses writes poetry for young people, edits anthologies and travels the country performing his poems. He is a great fan of Christmas. He lives in Sussex with his wife and two daughters.

Giles Pilbrow draws cartoons weekly for the *Sunday Times*, and regularly for *Private Eye* and the *Spectator* amongst others. He has written for and produced numerous series of *Spitting Image* and *The Big Breakfast*. He has also written and illustrated four other children's books.

*Also available from Macmillan*

THE SECRET LIVES OF TEACHERS
Poems chosen by Brian Moses

*MORE* SECRET LIVES OF TEACHERS
Poems chosen by Brian Moses

PARENT-FREE ZONE
Poems chosen by Brian Moses

ALIENS STOLE MY UNDERPANTS
Poems chosen by Brian Moses

SCHOOL TRIPS
Poems chosen by Brian Moses

DON'T LOOK AT ME IN THAT TONE OF VOICE
Poems by Brian Moses

# WE THREE KINGS...

## Christmas Poems
## chosen by Brian Moses

*Illustrated by Giles Pilbrow*

MACMILLAN
CHILDREN'S BOOKS

First published 1998

by Macmillan Children's Books
a division of Macmillan Publishers Ltd
25 Eccleston Place, London SW1W 9NF
and Basingstoke

Associated companies throughout the world

ISBN 0 330 37055 3

3 5 7 9 8 6 4

A CIP catalogue record for this book is available from the British Library.

Printed by Mackays of Chatham plc, Chatham, Kent.

# Contents

# Xmas Caro

Noel
No-el
No el
No 'l'
Born is the king
Of Israe.

*Nick Toczek*

# Angels

We are made from light.
Called into being we burn
Brighter than the silver white
Of hot magnesium.
More sudden than yellow phosphorous.
We are the fire of heaven;
Blue flames and golden ether.

We are from stars.
Spinning beyond the farthest galaxy
In an instant gathered to this point
We shine, speak our messages and go,
Back to the brilliance.
We are not separate, not individual,
We are what we are made of. Only
Shaped sometimes into tall-winged warriors,
Our faces solemn as swords,
Our voices joy.

The skies are cold;
Suns do not warm us;
Fire does not burn itself.
Only once we touched you
And felt a human heat.
Once, in the brightness of the frost.
Above the hills, in glittering starlight,
Once, we sang.

*Jan Dean*

# This Year I Will Stay Awake

This year I will stay awake
all night long make no mistake.
On this Christmas Eve I'll keep
my eyes open, try to peep.
This year I won't drowse or dream
but be alert till Santa's been,
see just what he leaves and how
he fits down our chimney now,
how the presents all appear
hear the sleigh bells and reindeer.
This year I will not count sheep
but pretend to be asleep.
No catnaps or snoozing but I
won't drop off and get some shut-eye.

This year there will be no slumber
I won't let myself go under.
No forty winks or throwing zeds.
No blinking, kipping, heavy headszz. . .
This year I won't nod or doze
or let my heavy eyelids close.
This year I won't nod or doze
or let my heavy eyelids close
or let my heavy eyelids close
or let my he..avy eye..li..ds clo..se
or let my he..avy eye..liiids clo..zzzzzzzzzzzzzzzzzzzz

*Paul Cookson*

# The First Christmas

It never snows at Christmas in that dry and dusty land.
Instead of freezing blizzards, there are palms and
    drifting sands,
and years ago a stable and a most unusual star
and three wise men who followed it, by camel, not by car,
while, sleepy on the quiet hills, a shepherd gave a cry.
He'd seen a crowd of angels in the silent starlit sky.
In the stable, ox and ass stood very still and calm
and gazed upon the baby, safe and snug, in Mary's arms.
And Joseph, lost in shadows, face lit by an oil lamp's glow
stood wondering, that first Christmas Day, two thousand
    years ago.


*Marian Swinger*

# Father Christmas

Dear Father Christmas,
Please bring me someone –

with a funny grin
that lets love in,

with a tender kiss
that makes me shiver
and feel warm inside,

with lovely brown
cocker-spaniel eyes,

with magic in her fingertips
like Paul Daniels
and riddles and jokes
and games,

with a world of love
to share.

Dear Father Christmas,
Please bring Daddy someone
too.


*Roger Stevens*

# Two Traffic Wardens
## on Christmas Eve

*Nabbed any good ones yet?*
Too right I have, a big fat geezer
with a white beard, wearing a red suit
and he's only trying to park
some kind of open truck on a double yellow line.

*So you says to him push off?*
Too right I did, I says to him 'Oi
what do you think you are playing at here, old son? Eh?
This is a restricted zone, you can't park that thing here
especially with all those animals.'

*Animals? What animals?*
Horrible great big deer things with vicious horns
and he keeps laughing and saying Ho Ho Ho
I says to him, 'You'll soon stop laughing
when I write out this parking ticket, old lad.'

*Nice one Stan, so what happened then?*
One of those nasty great deer things
really ugly looking he was, with a shiny red hooter
only goes and eats my parking ticket
and tries to eat the rest of the pad as well as my hat.

*Cheeky so and so, I hope you told him what for.*
I did, I can tell you, I says 'Oi! What's your game then?'
And he turns round and goes 'Ho Ho Ho' back at me
tells me he's some kind of van driver
with a load of kids' toys and stuff to deliver.

*So what? A double yellow line's a double yellow line.*
Exactly, I soon told him, silly old fool
looked him straight in the eye and wrote out a ticket
on the back of a shopping list I had handy
'Who do you think you are?' I said, 'Father Christmas?'


*David Harmer*

# December Moon

The moon has come out too soon,
it's still the middle of the afternoon
and the day shows no sign of darkness.

What is the moon doing,
sneaking into the sky when it's light?

What is the moon playing at?
Couldn't it sleep?
Has its alarm clock rung too soon?

Do we see the moon this early
In June or September?

Or does December bring a special moon,
a let's-get-these-nights-over-soon moon,
a can't-wait-for-Christmas-to-come moon?


*Brian Moses*

# Dear Father Christmas

Dear Father Christmas
This year please bring me
A pet rhinoc . . .
rhisoser . . .
rhinisus
rhinsiocerus
rhisky hoperus
rhibsipoperus
er . . .
I've changed my mind.
Bring me a rabbit instead.

*Roger Stevens*

# Dear Father Christmas

I'd like a hat (*without* a pompom),
new trainers in bright blue;
some money or a CD
and a personal stereo too.
But . . .
    *we've got no chimney!*

The most gigantic chocolate bar
to eat instead of tea;
my own phone to ring my friends
without Dad timing me.
But . . .
    *we've got no chimney!*

*P.S. Please could you use
    the cat flap?*

*Tracey Blance*

# Just Before Christmas

Down the Holloway Road on the top of the bus
On the just-before-Christmas nights we go,
Allie and me and all of us,
And we look at the lit-up shops below.
Orange and yellow the fruit stalls glow,
Store windows are sploshed with sort-of-snow,
And Santa's a poor old so-and-so,
With his sweating gear and his sack in tow,
And Christ . . . mas is coming!

At the front of the top of the lit-up bus
Way down the Holloway Road we ride,
Allie and me and all of us,
And the butchers chop and lop with pride,
And the turkeys squat with their stuffing inside
By ropes of sausages soon to be fried,
And every door is open wide
As down the road we growl or glide
And Christ . . . mas is coming!

All at the front of the top of the bus,
Far down the Holloway Road we roar,
Allie and me and all of us,
And tellies are tinselled in every store,
With fairy lights over every door,
With glitter and crêpe inside, what's more,
And everyone seeming to say, 'For sure,
Christmas is coming as never before.'
Yes, Christ . . . mas is coming!

*Kit Wright*

# Christmas at Four Winds Farm

With the tambourine tinkle of ice on the moor
and the winter moon white as a bone,
my grandad and his father
set out to bring Christmas home.

A wild winter wizard had grizzled the gorse
and spangled the splinter-sharp leaves,
when the light of their wind-swinging lantern
found a magical Christmas tree.

From the glittering town at the end of the dale
the carols grew sweeter and bolder,
as my grandad's smiling father
carried Christmas home on his shoulder.

*Maureen Haselhurst*

23

# The Crowd Scene

They say I can't act,
they say I can't dance.
They say I can't sing
but teacher won't give me a chance.

*So I'm in the crowd scene again.*

I asked to be a shepherd,
I begged to be a king.
I said that I'd play any part,
any persons, any thing!

*But I'm in the crowd scene again.*

I wanted to be an angel
but all of Mum's sheets were blue.
I even asked to be Joseph
but Mary said, 'Ugh, not you . . .'

*So I'm in the crowd scene again.*

I open and close my mouth,
teacher told me not to sing.
I move from place to place
and I watch and learn everything.

So if ever someone is absent,
I'll know it all by heart.
That's when I'll step from the crowd scene
to play my proper part.

*Brian Moses*

# Just Doing My Job

I'm one of Herod's Henchmen.
We don't have much to say,
We just charge through the audience
In a Henchman sort of way.

We all wear woolly helmets
To hide our hair and ears,
And Wellingtons sprayed silver
To match our tinfoil spears.

Our swords are made of cardboard
So blood will not be spilled
If we trip and stab a parent
When the hall's completely filled.

We don't look *very* scary,
We're mostly small and shy,
And some of us wear glasses,
But we give the thing a try.

We whisper Henchman noises
While Herod hunts for strangers,
And then we all charge out again
Like nervous Power Rangers.

Yet when the play is over
And Miss is out of breath
We'll charge like Henchmen through the hall
And scare our mums to death.

*Clare Bevan*

# Christmas Travellers

The frost was hard,
   the snowdrifts deep,
      when shepherds left
         their flock of sheep
            and glimpsed the child
          asleep,
              asleep.

               A new star shone
           on three Wise Men.
        Each wore a cloak
     and diadem.
   From far
they came to
Bethlehem.


*Wes Magee*

# Heart Stuff

Mums and dads they tell you all this stuff
And some of it's OK and some of it is guff.
There's the fairy who takes teeth – that's a story and a half
A sort of magic dentist; gives you cash for fangs –  a laugh.
The Father Christmas thing – you know the score –
I've looked out for him, I've squinted out of duvets,
Pretended sleep, but kept watch on the door,
But still I've never seen him. Never will,
My mother says. This Christmas thing, this Jesus stuff
That's strange stuff. Big stuff. After all, a star . . .
. . . Not every baby gets a welcome from the sky.
It makes you wonder. Makes you cry
To think what happened then.
If you ask me, I'd say he had it rough.
If he was all that meek and mild, how come he was so tough?
Dads and mums they tell you stuff,
Some sticks and some goes in one ear, then out.
They go on, don't they? My mum can't half shout.
But some stuff's special, like this Christmas thing.
You hear it in your heart . . . sounds daft – it's not, you know.
I keep remembering a marvellous baby in the shining snow.


*Jan Dean*

# A Route for Santa

Dear Santa,
            To get to me
make your way across the North Sea,
or, if you're feeling rushed and frantic,
come direct across the Atlantic.
Just as you approach UK
crack your whip and turn your sleigh.
(*Please be quick, yes, don't delay!*)
Giddy your reindeer up to a ton,
check your map and find the A1.
Just keep going. Fly on down.
Turn off left near Tiny Town.
Sleepy Village is off to the right –
look out for our front-door light.
Take the turn at Bendy Lane,
take next left, then left again.
We're the house with the yellow gate.
(*Hurry, please, it's hard to wait!*)

I'll leave some wine and a warm mince-pie,
as I know it's cold up there in the sky.
You'll find them next to the Christmas Tree.
Now this is how you'll get to *me*:
To reach my room you take the stair –
the third step's loose, so do take care.
Climb right up to the second floor
and tiptoe in through the bedroom door:
my door's red, the other's blue –
that one leads to the upstairs loo.
I'm sorry if the floorboards creak,
and probably my door will squeak
(*but I promise not to wake and peek*).
I'll leave a stocking at the end of my bed,
and, for bigger presents, a box instead.
I hope this route is plain and clear,
(*I couldn't wait another year*).
And, yes, I really have been good.
I helped to make the Christmas pud.
Looking forward to Christmas Eve
(*of course, you know I do believe . . .*).

Timmy Hope, Sleepy Village, UK

*Tony Mitton*

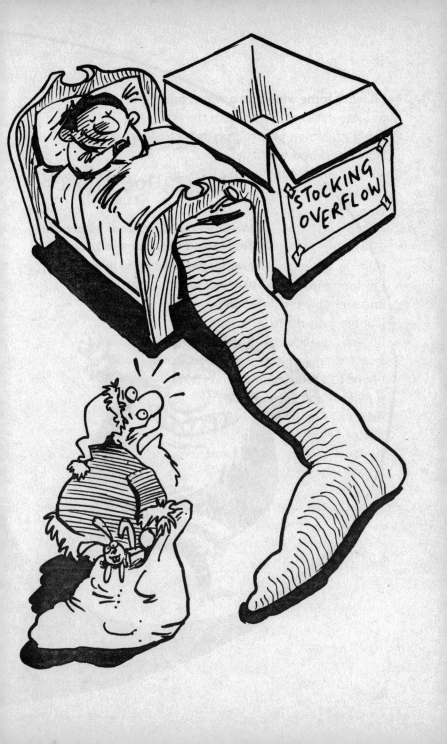

# Santa: Ace Guy
# or Strange Bloke?

Shows up every Christmas without fail.
Always knows what you've asked for.
Never forgets where you live.
Takes nothing in return:
Ace guy.

Strange bloke:
Answers everything with a 'Ho, ho, ho!'
Nowhere to be seen from January to November.
Thought to live at the North Pole with *elves*
    and *reindeers*.
And above all, he gives away loads of
    presents to complete strangers.

*James Carter*

# A Christmaths Mystery Solved

However hard you try to stay awake,
however vigilantly you peep,
you will never see Father Christmas delivering your presents.
Do you know why?
There's no special trick,
It's just simple arithmetic.

See,
at the equator the Earth is about 25,000 miles in circumference
and Father Christmas has 24 hours to deliver the presents.

Now if Father Christmas travelled only around the equator,
in order to get around it in 24 hours
he would have to travel at
(put that calculator away!)
more than 1000 miles an hour.

But Father Christmas doesn't travel
only around the equator.
He covers a good deal more of the Earth's surface as well,
even visiting liners on the high seas.

In fact, by making all the necessary detours,
during those 24 hours Father Christmas
travels thousands of times more
than just the girth of the Earth.

To sum up then,
on Christmas night
Father Christmas travels thousands of times faster
than a thousand miles per hour
(that's millions of miles per hour)
on his delivery round,
which is faster than any eye can see.

Now can you see why no one has ever seen
Father Christmas delivering presents?

*Philip Waddell*

# We Are Not Alone

Captain's Log. Starship Saturnalian.
Earth year 2030, day 358 –
The new drive worked! We've tracked the alien
spacecraft that vanished from Earth's orbit late

last night. We followed its fantastic leap
across the galaxy and now can see
its sledge-like shape dropping in steep
descent to a planet. Incredibly

a single cosmonaut whose suit glows red
clings to its tail and holds long ropes to steer
a group of prancing creatures: from each head
sprout aerials that make them look like deer.

The planet's steaming, its surface smooth and
dark as Christmas pudding. Prepare to land!

*Dave Calder*

BEFORE

AFTER

# Reindeer Report

Chimneys: colder.
Flightpaths: busier.
Driver: Christmas (F)
Still baffled by postcodes.

Children: more
And stay up later.
Presents: heavier.
Pay: frozen.

Mission in spite
Of all this
Accomplished:
Merry Christmas!

*U.A. Fanthorpe*

# Early Christmas Morning

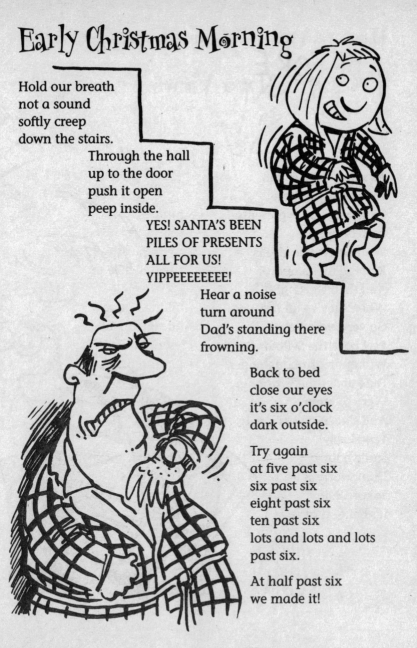

Hold our breath
not a sound
softly creep
down the stairs.

Through the hall
up to the door
push it open
peep inside.

YES! SANTA'S BEEN
PILES OF PRESENTS
ALL FOR US!
YIPPEEEEEEEE!

Hear a noise
turn around
Dad's standing there
frowning.

Back to bed
close our eyes
it's six o'clock
dark outside.

Try again
at five past six
six past six
eight past six
ten past six
lots and lots and lots
past six.

At half past six
we made it!

*David Harmer*

43

# How to Open Your Christmas Presents: Two Views

*One*

It's best to go
As slowly as you can.
Take plenty of time
To arrange your presents
In neat piles
While everyone else is
Ripping theirs apart . . .
And then start only
When they've all finished.
Go very, very slowly . . .
Peel back the Sellotape
Without tearing the paper,
Peek under the wrapping
Every so often,
And slide it off very, very,
*Very* slowly . . .
Smile a lot.
Don't worry if it
Takes all day;
It's better that way.

## Two

Quick, quick,
Grab those presents
As fast as you can,
Don't, don't, don't wait!
Don't hesitate!
Rip, tear,
Anywhere, who cares
What others think,
And don't worry about
Those slowcoaches who
Take their time . . .
Go very, very,
*Very* quickly,
Especially if your presents
Are wrapped extra-thickly . . .
Remember, you haven't
Got all year . . .
Christmas day's today
And only today . . .
It's better that way.

*Tony Bradman*

45

# The Great Present Muddle

Santa's in a muddle,
Santa's in a mess.
He muddled all the labels
. . . and Father got a dress.

Mother got some football boots,
Uncle got a bra,
Auntie got some roller skates,
and grandad got a star.
My cousin wanted knickers,
but she got a big white rat.
Arthur asked for whiskey
and got a silly hat.

Johnny said,
'A racing bike'
but Johnny got a rose.
Grandma got a football
And Frank's designer clothes.

Oh what an awful muddle!
Which belongs to who?

I'm sure you know the answer,
so I leave it up to you.

*Peter Dixon*

# The Best Christmas Present Ever

Underneath the Christmas tree
A present there for all to see
Neatly wrapped, just for me . . .
A rocking horse!

There before my very eyes
My own magical surprise
and, it seems, the perfect size . . .
A rocking horse!

I thought I heard the sound of scrunching
And it was my present crunching
From within the paper munching . . .
A rocking horse?

The tattered wrapping on the ground
It stood and made the strangest sound
And barking, chased its tail around . . .
A rocking horse?!

The greatest gift I ever had
An Irish Wolfhound from my dad
'By heck! It took some wrapping, lad!'
Better than a rocking horse!

*Paul Cookson and David Harmer*

# The Christmas Murder!

Who pulled Sooty's head off?

We needed an answer
when a headless Sooty was discovered
in the debris of Christmas wrapping.

We set up an interview room
and asked everyone the same question:
Where were you when Sooty met his doom?

All the suspects came and went
as we checked their alibis:
Little brother was having a tantrum,
    could he have done it
        in a fit of pique?

                Or sister, playing with Barbies,
                 was it jealousy?

                Both were keeping tight-lipped.

We interviewed the turkey
but the bird refused to squawk,
and even though we trod on her tail,
the cat wouldn't squeal.

It was just like Cluedo:
Was it Mum in the kitchen
with the carving knife
or Dad in the lounge
with the rope?

Nobody knew.
There were no clues.

But me, I reckon it was Sweep,
although we couldn't get a squeak
out of him!

*Brian Moses*

# My Friend Izzy

My friend Izzy
For Christmas she got
A spider ladder
For helping stranded spiders out of the bath,
A fly parachute
For flies whose wings are too wet to fly,
Four sets of non-stick fly boots
To stop flies getting stuck in webs,
Some sticky vegetarian sausages
To stick on the webs instead of the flies,
Some tiny mirrors
For ladybirds to count their own spots
(In case they are lucky),
A box of minuscule splints
For centipedes with broken legs,
And some honeycomb
To give back to the bees.
My friend Izzy
She's a bit odd you know.

*Diana Riddell*

# On the Thirteenth Day of Christmas My True Love Phoned Me Up . . .

Well, I suppose I should be grateful, you've obviously gone
to a lot of trouble and expense – or maybe off your head.
Yes, I did like the birds – the small ones anyway were fun
if rather messy, but now the hens have roosted on my bed
and the rest are nested on the wardrobe. It's hard to sleep
with all that cooing, let alone the cackling of the geese
whose eggs are everywhere, but mostly in a broken
 smelly heap
on the sofa. No, why should I mind? I can't get any
 peace
anywhere – the lounge is full of drummers thumping
 tom-toms

and sprawling lords crashed out from manic leaping. The
kitchen is crammed with cows and milkmaids and smells of
    a million stink-bombs
and enough sour milk to last a year. The pipers? I'd
    forgotten them –
they were no trouble, I paid them and they went. But I can't
    get rid
of these young ladies. They won't stop dancing or turn the
    music down
and they're always in the bathroom, squealing as they skid
across the flooded floor. No, I don't need a plumber round,
it's just the swans – where else can they swim? Poor things,
I think they're going mad, like me. When I went to wash my
hands one ate the soap, another swallowed the gold rings.
And the pear tree died. Too dry. So thanks for nothing, love.
    Goodbye.

*Dave Calder*

# A Christmas Tree is For Christmas Not For Ever

Nobody wants a Christmas tree after Christmas
Nobody wants a tree that's lost its looks.
Nobody wants a tree without a star on top
Nobody wants to bother about its roots.

Nobody wants tired tinsel after Christmas.
Nobody wants the mistletoe hanging there.
Nobody wants torn wrapping paper either.
Nobody wants to find holly on their chair.

Nobody wants the tree without its needles
Nobody wants the fairy with her wings all bent
Nobody wants to start the basic clearing up.
Nobody wants to remember where things went.

Nobody wants to remember that twelfth night's here.
Nobody wants to take the baubles off the tree.
Nobody wants to put the cards away
. . . but . . .
everybody's going to help before they get their tea!!

*Janis Priestley*

# The Big, Fab, Brill, Magic, Neat, Wow Christmas Present!

Yesterday I went shopping
and bought my sister –
**a Christmas present.**

It had wheels that were – **BIG!**
It had flashing lights that were – **FAB!**
It had a dashboard that was – **BRILL!**
It had a supersonic siren that was – **MAGIC!**
It had working seat belts that were – **NEAT!**
It even had a remote control – **WOW!**
And **I know** because I tried it all out in the shop!!

The present was **excellent!**
The present was **mega** –
in fact **cool beans!**

But somehow on Christmas Day
my sister's face just
**didn't agree!**

*Ian Souter*